The Giant Turtle

Published, translated, and adapted by the
Buddhist Text Translation Society
Dharma Realm Buddhist University
Dharma Realm Buddhist Association
Burlingame, California U.S.A.

The Giant Turtle—English-only edition
A fictionalized version of "The Tortoise King," *Human Roots*,
Buddhist Text Translation Society, 1982.
Illustrations by Candy, age 9, with a little help from her friends.

Published by:
Buddhist Text Translation Society
1777 Murchison Drive
Burlingame, California 94010-4504

© 2000 Buddhist Text Translation Society
      Dharma Realm Buddhist University
      Dharma Realm Buddhist Association

First English edition 2000
First bilingual Chinese/English edition 2000
Second edition of both：2002
09 08 07 06 05 04 03 02   10 9 8 7 6 5 4 3 2
ISBN 0-88139-314-2

Printed in Taiwan, R.O.C.

Addresses of the Dharma Realm Buddhist Association branches are listed at the back of this book.

Library of Congress Cataloging-in-Publication Data

The giant turtle
    p. cm.
   Summary: A traditional Buddhist tale about one of the Buddha's past lives as a giant turtle who carried forests, villages, rivers, and lakes on its back.
   ISBN 0-88139-314-2 (pbk. : alk. paper)
   1. Jataka stories, English. [1. Jataka stories.]

BQ1462.E5 G5 2000
294.3'82325--dc21

                                     00-022853

The Giant Turtle

Jataka Tales

The Jataka tales are stories that the Buddha told about the many times he was reborn on Earth, sometimes as a prince or a poor man, sometimes as an animal, a fish or a tree. These stories celebrate the joy, compassion, wisdom, and kindness that the Buddha showed in each of these lives as he helped others.

The Giant Turtle is one of the tales told by the Buddha to his disciples over 2,500 years ago.

The Giant Turtle

Once a long, long time ago, the Buddha came to the earth as a giant turtle king that ruled over all the animals in the deep blue sea. Everyday he swam among the colorful fish, the

pearly-white oysters, and the blue whales, helping them with their problems and wishing them well. Everyone was happy and peaceful in his kingdom of the sea.

6

One day he crawled onto the sandy beach to take a nap. Because he was so large, as large as a continent, he napped for a very long time--for thousands of years.

At night, the rain came, dropping tiny raindrops onto the turtle's back. *Drip*! *Drip*! The raindrops flowed down between the cracks on the turtle's great shell, forming sparkling rivers and lakes.

The turtle slept on.

In the mornings, the winds came up, blowing tiny grains of sand onto the turtle's back. *Whoo-sha! Whoo-sha!* The sand grains joined together, forming mountains and valleys.

The turtle slept on.

In the afternoons, the birds flew over, dropping tiny seeds onto the turtle's back. *Plink! Plink!* The seeds sprouted, and there on the turtle's back grew flowers and grass and trees.

The turtle slept on.

The sun warmed the turtle in the daytime.

The moon watched over him at night.

As time passed, spring, summer, autumn, and winter embraced the giant turtle, and the animals that lived on the turtle's back multiplied.

One day, a child wandered among the mountains and valleys to pick wild flowers. She didn't know she was walking on a turtle's back.

The next day she brought her family.

"This will be a good place to build a house," said the father, "we can grow rice and get salt from the sea."

The turtle slept on.

The next year another family moved to the little mountain on the turtle's back. Gradually more and more families came to live there.

Roads were built and merchants came to set up shops.

A prince built a palace.

The turtle slept on.

People pulled their carts and rode their carriages over the streets, cutting deep ruts into the turtle's shell. Their cities became heavy on his back, and their noises drummed in his ears. The fires they built burned his skin.

And so it went, until one day the giant turtle was awakened
by the pain from the fires. Wanting to cool himself, he began

to crawl toward the sea. He did not hear the people cry, "Earthquake! Earthquake!" He did not see them run hither and thither.

Upon reaching the sea, he immersed himself in the cool water
to ease the pain. When the dwellers on his back saw water
rising all around them, they screamed, "Flood! Flood! We
will drown!"

For the first time, the giant turtle realized that there were people living on his back. Not wanting to bring pain to them, he crawled back onto the beach.

For another thousand years, he let the fires burn his skin and the rumble of the city shake him. During the days he held back the tears, but at night he let them flow. So great was his pain and so silent were his tears, but no one knew of his sacrifice.

The day came when the turtle could no longer endure the pain. He decided that he needed to return to the sea. Slowly raising his head, he spoke to the people, "Don't be afraid. I won't hurt you. You see, I'm a giant turtle and you're living on my shell. I must go back into the water, or I'll die."

One by one, the people gathered their belongings and moved back onto the beach. The giant turtle eased the buildings and homes and the prince's palace off his back. The people created new villages and cities on the earth, and their lives went on as before.

All were grateful for the kindness of the giant turtle. They bowed to him and said, "For thousands of years, you've given us your back on which to build our world. You are a great king turtle! Surely, you will become a Buddha in the future."

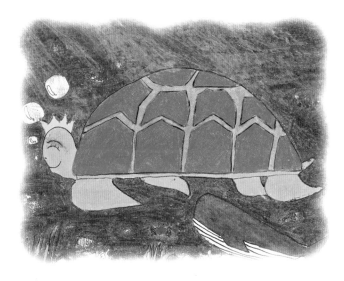

High above the turtle, birds circled and swooped down,
placing garlands of fragrant flowers around his neck.

Monkeys came and rubbed his sores with healing herbs, and elephants trumpeted sweet music to soothe his ears.

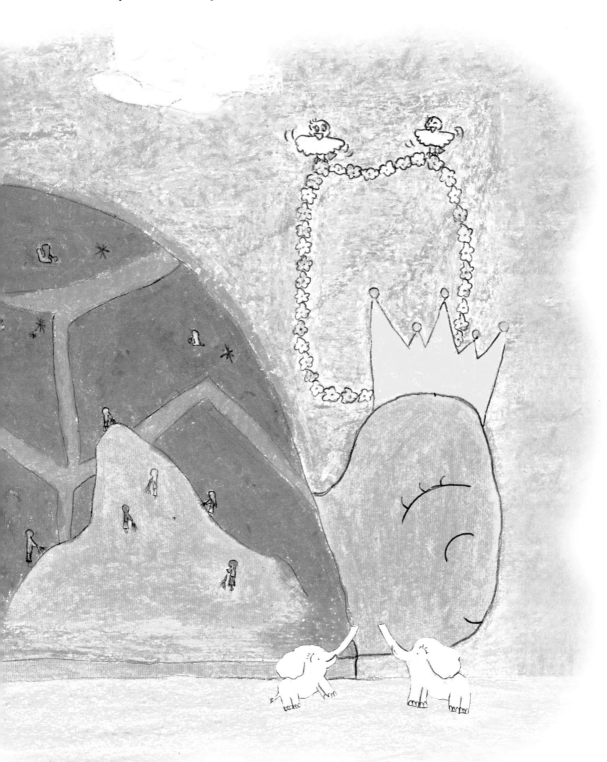

People swept the sand from his back with peacock feathers,
and the giant turtle crawled back into the sea.

After telling this tale, the Buddha said, "I was the king turtle and the people who lived on my back became my disciples."

The Dharma Realm Buddhist Association

The Dharma Realm Buddhist Association (DRBA) was founded by the Venerable Master Hsuan Hua in the United States of America in 1959 to bring the genuine teachings of the Buddha to the entire world. Its goals are to propagate the Proper Dharma, to translate the Mahayana Buddhist scriptures into the world's languages and to promote ethical education. The members of the Association guide themselves with six ideals established by the Venerable Master which are: no fighting, no greed, no seeking, no selfishness, no pursuing personal advantage, and no lying. They hold in mind the credo:

Freezing, we do not scheme.
Starving, we do not beg.
Dying of poverty, we ask for nothing.
According with conditions, we do not change.
Not changing, we accord with conditions.
We adhere firmly to our three great principles.
We renounce our lives to do the Buddha's work.
We take responsibility in molding our own destinies.
We rectify our lives to fulfill our role as members of the Sangha.
Encountering specific matters, we understand the principles.
Understanding the principles, we apply them in specific matters.
We carry on the single pulse of the patriarchs' mind-transmission.

During the decades that followed DRBA's establishment, international Buddhist communities such as Gold Mountain Monastery, the City of Ten Thousand Buddhas, the City of the Dharma Realm, and various other branch facilities were founded. All these operate under the traditions of the Venerable Master and through the auspices of the Dharma Realm Buddhist Association. Following the Buddhas' guidelines, the Sangha members in these monastic facilities maintain the practices of taking only one meal a day and of always wearing their precept sashes. Reciting the Buddha's name, studying the teachings, and practicing meditation, they dwell together in harmony and personally put into practice Shakyamuni Buddha's teachings. Reflecting Master Hua's emphasis on translation and education, the Association also sponsors an International Translation Institute, vocational training programs for Sangha and laity, Dharma Realm Buddhist University, and elementary and secondary schools.

The Way-places of this Association are open to sincere individuals of all races, religions, and nationalities. Everyone who is willing to put forth his or her best effort in nurturing humaneness, righteousness, merit, and virtue in order to understand the mind and see the nature is welcome to join in the study and practice.

Dharma Realm Buddhist Association
The City of Ten Thousand Buddhas

2001 Talmage Road, Talmage, CA 95481-0217 U.S.A.

Tel: (707) 462-0939   Fax: (707) 462-0949

• •

The International Translation Institute

1777 Murchison Drive, Burlingame, CA 94010-4504 U.S.A.
Tel: (650) 692-5912   Fax: (650) 692-5056

Institute for World Religions (at Berkeley Buddhist Monastery)

2304 McKinley Avenue, Berkeley, CA 94703 U.S.A.
Tel: (510) 848-3440   Fax: (510) 548-4551

Gold Mountain Monastery

800 Sacramento Street, San Francisco, CA 94108 U.S.A.
Tel: (415) 421-6117   Fax: (415) 788-6001

Gold Sage Monastery

11455 Clayton Road, San Jose, CA 95127 U.S.A.
Tel: (408) 923-7243   Fax: (408) 923-1064

The City of the Dharma Realm

1029 West Capitol Avenue, West Sacramento, CA 95691 U.S.A.
Tel/Fax: (916) 374-8268

Gold Wheel Monastery

235 North Avenue 58, Los Angeles, CA 90042 U.S.A.
Tel/Fax: (323) 258-6668

Long Beach Monastery

3361 East Ocean Boulevard, Long Beach, CA 90803 U.S.A.
Tel/Fax: (562) 438-8902

Blessings, Prosperity, and Longevity Monastery

4140 Long Beach Boulevard, Long Beach, CA 90807 U.S.A.
Tel/Fax: (562) 595-4966

Avatamsaka Hermitage

11721 Beall Mountain Road, Potomac, MD 20854-1128 U.S.A.
Tel/Fax: (301) 299-3693

Gold Summit Monastery

233 First Avenue West, Seattle, WA 98119 U.S.A.

Tel/Fax: (206) 217-9320

Gold Buddha Monastery

301 East Hastings Street, Vancouver, BC V6A 1P3 Canada

Tel/Fax: (604) 684-3754

Avatamsaka Monastery

1009 Fourth Avenue S.W., Calgary, AB T2P 0K8 Canada

Tel/Fax: (403) 234-0644

Dharma Realm Buddhist Books Distribution Society

11th Floor, 85 Chung-hsiao E. Road, Sec. 6, Taipei, R.O.C.

Tel: (02) 2786-3022, 2786-2474   Fax: (02) 2786-2674

Dharma Realm Sage Monastery

20, Tung-hsi Shan-chuang, Hsing-lung Village, Liu-kuei, Kaohsiung County, Taiwan, R.O.C.

Tel: (07) 689-3713   Fax: (07) 689-3870

Amitabha Monastery

7, Su-chien-hui, Chih-nan Village, Shou-feng, Hualien County, Taiwan, R.O.C.

Tel: (03) 865-1956   Fax:(03) 865-3426

Tze Yun Tung Temple

Batu 5 1/2, Jalan Sungai Besi, Salak Selatan, 57100 Kuala Lumpur, Malaysia

Tel: (03)782-6560   Fax:(03) 780-1272

Lotus Vihara

136, Jalan Sekolah, 45600 Batang Berjuntai, Selangor Darul Ehsan, Malaysia

Tel: (03) 871-9439

Deng Bi An Temple

161, Jalan Ampang, 50450 Kuala Lumpur, Malaysia

Tel: (03) 2164-8055   Fax: (03)2163-7118

Buddhist Lecture Hall

31 Wong Nei Chong Road, Top Floor, Happy Valley, Hong Kong

Tel/Fax: 2572-7644

One day he crawled onto the sandy beach to take a nap.
Because he was so large, as large as a continent, he napped
for a very long time--for thousands of years.